American Tall Tales

Based on Traditional Stories
Adapted by Lauren Myracle

SCHOLASTIC INC.

New York   Toronto   London   Auckland   Sydney
Mexico City   New Delhi   Hong Kong   Buenos Aires

Illustrations
Sterling Hundley

Copyright © 2003 by Scholastic Inc.
All rights reserved. Published by Scholastic Inc.
Printed in the U.S.A.

ISBN 0-439-59782-x

SCHOLASTIC, SCHOLASTIC ACTION, and associated logos and designs are trademarks and/or registered trademarks of Scholastic Inc.

LEXILE is a registered trademark of MetaMetrics, Inc.

3 4 5 6 7 8 9 10   23   12 11 10 09 08 07 06 05 04

Contents

Welcome to This Book

Have you ever told a story that was mostly true? Maybe you built it up a bit to impress your friends. Well, you're in good company.

People have been telling stories like this for ages. They're called "tall tales." Would you believe there was a man who could hammer faster than a machine? How about a woman who wore a mountain lion for a dress? Or a fireman who could fly from a burning building?

Believe it or not, there's a little bit of truth in each story. The only question is, how much?

Target Words These words will help you understand what makes these tales tall.

- **brave:** without fear in the face of danger

  Mose became a famous fireman because he was brave.

- **character:** having strong values and living up to them

  John Henry was a man of character.

- **exaggeration:** a statement that goes beyond the truth

  It's an exaggeration to say that Sally Ann got wet first when it rained because she was so tall.

Reader Tips Here's how to get the most out of this book.

- **Picture Clues** Use the illustrations to help you picture what you're reading. Look for picture details that exaggerate these tall-tale characters.

- **Draw Conclusions** As you read, think about the facts and details you learn about these characters. Put them together to draw a conclusion, or a new understanding, about these stories.

Meet the Characters

The characters in this book lived long ago. Back then, the United States was still young. That's when these stories got started. As the country grew, so did the stories. Here are the people who inspired them.

John Henry

A steel-driving man. He helped build the country's railroads. John Henry was strong and proud. The tall tales say he could hammer faster than a machine.

Mose

A firefighting superhero. In the early days of this country, most buildings were made of wood. So fires were a big problem. But Mose came to the rescue no matter what. The tall tales say he could even fly.

Sally Ann Thunder

An early settler in Tennessee. The land was still wild. It took tough people to settle there. Sally was one of the toughest. The tall tales say she once gave the Earth a swift kick.

CHAPTER

John Henry: Steel-Driving Man

No one could swing a hammer like John Henry.

John Henry was born with a hammer in his hand. That's the honest truth. He came into the world like any other baby. But in his hand was a big, shiny hammer.

Well, John Henry grew up, as all babies do. He headed into the world and took his hammer with him.

One day, he met a work crew. The crew was building a railroad. Hammers flashed in the air. John Henry grinned. This was where he wanted to be.

"Excuse me," he said to the boss. "I'd like to help build this fine railroad."

"I've already got a crew," the boss said. "Why should I hire you?"

"Because I want to pound some steel," John Henry said. "I'll be the best steel driver you've ever seen."

"I'll believe that when I see it," the boss said. He turned to his crew. "If he's going to hammer, someone has to hold the spike. Anyone willing?"

The workers shook their heads. They were all afraid.

"He'll miss it for sure," one man said. "He'll smash my hands!"

"Now wait just a minute," John Henry said. "I'll hit that spike. And I'll hit it straight. I'll pound it right into the track."

The men just stared at the ground. Then Little Willie stepped forward. He wasn't tough and strong like the others. But he was **brave**.

Heads Up!

Railroad tracks were nailed down with giant steel spikes. In John Henry's time, workers had to hammer them in by hand. That's why they were called "steel drivers."

John Henry raised his hammer as high as he could.

"I'll hold the spike," he said. "But listen. Take it easy this first time, okay?"

John Henry raised his hammer as high as he could. He brought it down like lightning. BLAM! He drove that spike right into the track.

Little Willie whistled. He had pulled his hand away just in time. The workers dropped their jaws. The boss's eyes grew huge.

"You, sir, have a job," he said to John Henry. From then on, John Henry hammered from dawn till dusk. No job was too hard. No job was too big.

"You can count on me," John Henry said. "I'm the best steel driver there's ever been."

Heads Up!

John Henry drives the spike into the track with just one swing. The other workers are stunned. What does that tell you about John Henry?

John Henry Against the Machine

Who will win the contest?

One day, the crew's tracks reached a mountain. Something would have to be done.

The boss shook his head. "We're going to have to dig a tunnel," he said. "I don't know how we'll do it."

Just then, a stranger stepped forward. Behind him was a big machine.

"This here's a steam drill," the man said. "It can cut right through rock. It's faster than six men combined."

"Not if I'm one of the men," said John Henry.

The men decided to hold a contest. It would be John Henry against the machine. John Henry on one side and the steam drill on the other.

"I'll die before I let that machine win," John

Henry said. "A man is a man. But a machine is nothing but a machine."

So Little Willie got into place. He held the biggest spike he had against the mountain's side. Then he nodded to John Henry.

John Henry lifted his hammer. The stranger flipped a switch. And the race was on.

John Henry grunted. His hammer swung through the air. Clang! Bang! Again and again, he struck that spike as hard as he could. Pieces of rock flew through the air. And in no time at all, a hole started to grow.

The machine **shrieked**. It hissed and roared as it dug into the mountain.

Sweat ran down John Henry's back. Workers threw cold water over the men. They even poured water on John Henry's hammer. They were afraid it might burst into flames!

Heads Up!

Look up the word shriek *in the glossary. What might make a person shriek? Why do you think the writer chose this word to describe how the machine sounds?*

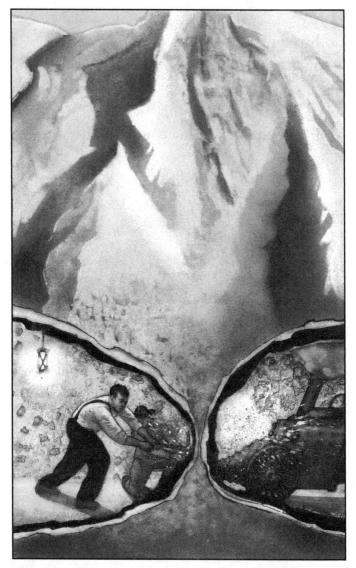

The machine doesn't stand a chance against John Henry.

The race went on for hours. Slowly, the tunnel opened up. Dust and rock showered down. John Henry and the machine were neck and neck.

John Henry's breath grew **ragged**. His heart pounded. Little Willie frowned. "John Henry," he asked, "how are you feeling?"

"I feel fine," John Henry said. "I feel powerful. And I feel free."

Then he saw the machine pulling ahead. "Give me another hammer," he said.

Little Willie put one in his other hand. John Henry started swinging both hammers at once. He moved so fast, he was a blur.

The machine didn't stand a chance. Why? A machine is nothing but a machine. But John Henry was a man.

The machine **shuddered**. It coughed and groaned. Finally, it stopped altogether. The men

---

Heads Up!

How is John Henry able to dig a tunnel through a mountain? Look at the picture on page 14 to get an idea.

could barely believe what just happened. The contest was over. John Henry had beaten the machine.

John Henry looked dazed. He wiped the sweat from his brow.

Little Willie reached out to his friend. "John Henry? Are you okay?"

"I'm a little tired," John Henry said. "But I feel powerful. I feel free."

Then John Henry sank to the ground. He closed his eyes forever. His hammer was still in his hand.

Heads Up!

This story shows the difference between a man and a machine. How would you describe that difference?

Will the Real John Henry Please Stand Up?

The real John Henry lived in the late 1800s. Of course, he wasn't born with a hammer in his hand. But he did build railroads in West Virginia.

John Henry was a good man. He was honest. And he worked harder than anyone. People looked up to him because he was strong. But they also admired him because he was a man of **character.** All this made for some great stories.

People say the contest between John Henry and the steam drill really did happen. The tunnel was called Big Bend Tunnel. John Henry beat the steam drill. But it took all he had. He died shortly after. He was thirty-four years old.

Mose: Firefighting Superhero

When there's a fire to fight, call on Mose.

Mose was the fastest firefighter ever. When the alarm bell rang, he didn't waste a second. He threw his boots out the window. He jumped out after them. He landed inside them on the sidewalk. And he took off just like a bolt of lightning! Mose was that fast.

He was strong, too. He could lift just about anything. If a heavy door was in his way, no problem. He'd toss it aside like a toothpick. Or a heavy metal stove? He'd roll up his sleeves and toss it away like an old tin can.

Mose could even lift something heavier, if he had to. Listen up. And I'll tell you exactly what happened.

One day, Mose was hanging out with his firefighting buddies. They were sitting in the fire station, telling jokes. Just then, the alarm bell rang. A building was on fire!

Mose grabbed his gear and **bolted** from the station. He knew every second mattered. Lives were in danger! He had to help!

But halfway there, he ran into trouble. The street was blocked by a **streetcar.**

The firefighters could not pull the big water pump through. And without the pump, there'd be no water.

"Hey! Move that streetcar!" shouted Mose. "We've got a fire to put out!"

"I would if I could," said the driver. "But I can't! Something is wrong."

"It's true!" yelled one of the passengers. "We are completely stuck!"

So Mose hopped onto the tracks. He lifted that streetcar as easy as you please. The passengers all screamed in fear. But Mose held on tight.

Heads Up!

Close your eyes and try to picture Mose lifting up a streetcar. Then check out the drawing on page 20. Is that what you saw?

Mose moves that streetcar out of the way.

He moved that streetcar out of the way. Then he sat it down with barely a thunk.

The passengers cheered when they saw they were safe. "Thank you!" they cried. "Three cheers for Mose!"

But Mose was hardly listening. He was too busy worrying about the fire. It was growing bigger and hotter every second.

"No trouble at all," he said. "But I can't stop to chat. Step lively, boys! We've got a fire to put out!"

Mose Goes Airborne

A little girl is trapped.
Will Mose be able to save her?

Now this fire was bad. The building that was burning was five stories high. And on the top floor was a little girl. She was trapped! She couldn't get down!

When Mose got there, he started to worry. This was the worst fire he'd ever seen. The building was crackling and popping. Dark smoke poured from every window. Flames licked all the way to the roof.

Mose and his men dragged the water pump to a hydrant. They hooked it up. The water began to flow. Mose kept a tight hold on the firehose. But it wasn't easy.

"Stand back, everyone!" he called. Water shot from the hose. Mose aimed at the burning building. But the flames were too **fierce**. They just kept getting bigger.

"My daughter!" the little girl's mother cried. "You've got to save my daughter!"

"Help!" the little girl screamed. "I'm scared! Please save me!"

Mose grabbed a ladder and started to climb toward the little girl.

"Mose, you can't go up there!" one of the other firefighters said. "It's too dangerous. It's hotter than an oven!"

But Mose kept climbing. If someone needed help, he would do all he could. He would never give up. No way.

Mose reached the little girl. He pulled her from the window. But now his ladder was on fire. He had to think quick!

—Heads Up!—
The building crackles. Smoke pours from the windows. And flames lick the roof. Use these details to picture the fire.

With the girl in his arms, Mose hops onto the chunk of roof.

He had a crazy idea. But it just might work. He climbed on top of the building. With his axe, he chopped at the roof. He chopped off a nice big piece. Then he grabbed the little girl. "Hold on!" he yelled.

With the little girl in his arms, Mose hopped onto the chunk of roof. On it they slid off the building and sailed into the sky. They left flames far behind. They flew past houses. They flew past schools.

"Go, Mose!" the firefighters yelled. "Easy now! Keep it steady!"

"Whoo-eee!" Mose **hollered**.

Soon Mose caught sight of a nearby river. Mose steered the piece of roof toward it. He held the little girl tight. They hit the water, and SPLASH! A giant wave rose higher and higher into the air.

"Watch out, everyone!" cried the firefighters. "It's coming our way!"

Heads Up!

"Whoo-eee!" sounds more excited than scared. How do you think Mose feels about his work?

The wave crashed down on the building. Sizzle! Hiss! Fizz! The fire went out. And everyone cheered.

"Shucks," Mose said when he climbed on shore. He handed the little girl to her mother. "I was only doing my duty."

Will the Real Mose Please Stand Up?

Mose was a real firefighter. His full name was Mose Humphreys. He lived in New York in the 1800s.

Back then, fires were a big problem. That's because most buildings were made of wood. One big fire could wipe out a whole town.

People loved Mose because he was strong and brave. He would risk his life to save someone else. That's why people told stories about him. He did whatever he could to keep them safe.

Now, maybe the stories got carried away. Chances are Mose never flew through the air. But that didn't matter. What mattered was Mose's brave **spirit**. People told these stories to show he was a hero.

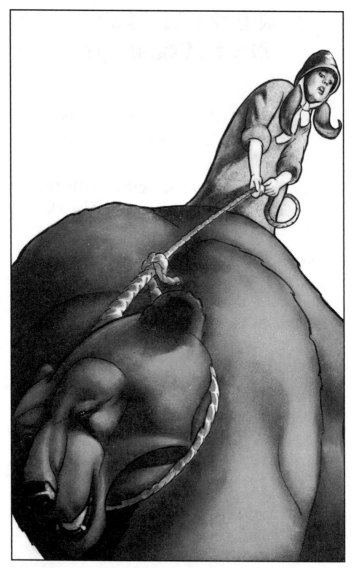

Sally Ann has a pet bear named Death-Hug.

Sally Ann Thunder: Wild Woman of the Woods

Don't mess with Sally Ann and Death-Hug!

Have you heard of a man named Davy Crockett? People called him "king of the wild **frontier.**" Davy loved adventure. He helped tame Tennessee back when Tennessee was wild.

Back then, the place was crawling with bears, bobcats, and mountain lions. The forests were as thick as could be. That is, until Davy came along. He helped clear the land for farming.

But that's only part of the story. He didn't do it alone.

Davy had a wife, you see. Her name was Sally Ann Thunder. She was one tough lady. She wore a hornets' nest for a hat. And her dress was made from a mountain lion.

Sally Ann was tall, too. So tall that she got wet first whenever it rained. And she was quick. So quick that she could jump over her own shadow. And, she could dance better than anyone in the whole U. S. of A.

Sally Ann also had a pet bear named Death-Hug. At first, Death-Hug was Davy's pet. But Death-Hug liked Sally Ann better. You see, she smelled better. Plus, she could dance. And everyone knows that bears love to dance.

So Davy just shook his head and found another pet. Because you don't argue with a bear. Not if you know what's good for you. Instead, Davy found a sweet little kitten, soft and fuzzy.

Well, one winter morning, Sally Ann went for a walk. She took Death-Hug with her. She threw a rope around his neck for a leash. And she held on tight.

They hadn't gone far when Sally Ann started to shiver. It was freezing cold outside. It was so cold that Sally Ann's shadow froze to the ground! She couldn't pull it up. So she left it behind.

She tried to start a fire with her hands. She bashed her knuckles together like two stones.

But the sparks from her knuckles froze in the air. That's how cold it was.

Something awful had happened for sure. The Sun froze as it was trying to rise! Then Earth began to shiver, too. It froze stiff in its tracks, just like the Sun.

"Darn it all!" Sally Ann said. "We've got a problem here. And someone's got to fix it."

She thought hard. Then she smiled. She knew just the person to do it.

Sally Ann Saves the Planet

The Earth needs a good swift kick.
And Sally Ann is just the person to do it.

Now, Sally Ann wasn't just tough. She was smart, too. She knew Earth needed help. And she wasn't about to wait for someone else to do it. All she had to do was come up with a plan.

"Let me think," Sally Ann said. "First, I've got to warm up this freezing planet. But how?"

She looked at Death-Hug and grinned. "I've got a job for you, old buddy," she said.

She let Death-Hug off his leash. He blinked at her, surprised. Then he started to run. He ran fast and free and full of joy!

"Yippee!" yelled Sally Ann.

She chased after him as quickly as she could. Round and round they went. Death-Hug roared. Sally Ann hollered.

The other animals moved out of the way. But Sally Ann and Death-Hug ran and ran.

Finally, Death-Hug wore himself out. He panted, trying to catch his breath. Then he flopped his big, warm body down to rest.

And do you know what happened? The warmth from his body soaked into the ground. Earth began to heat up.

Sally Ann smiled. Her plan was working.

"Come on, you lazy thing," she said to the cold, sleepy Earth.

She raised her foot. She took a deep breath. And she gave Earth one giant-sized kick. Dirt flew high into the air.

"Go on, now! Get moving!" she yelled.

Well, Earth groaned and creaked. It stirred itself up from its cold night's sleep. Slowly, slowly, it started to turn.

Heads Up!

The words groan, creak, *and* slowly *tell you how Earth moves. Do you think it is easy or hard to make Earth move? Why?*

Sally Ann gives Earth one giant-sized kick.

Then Sally Ann moved on to the Sun. "It's your turn now!" she called. "Rise and shine, you lazy, old fireball!"

The Sun didn't want a kick from Sally Ann. It did just what it was told. It rose up into the sky, hot and bright. And in no time at all, the world was full of light.

Sally Ann put her hands on her hips. She looked around at the world. And she grinned at what she had done.

"Nice work," she said to Death-Hug.

Death-Hug just snored. So she tossed him over her shoulders. And she carried him all the way back home.

When they got there, Sally Ann pulled something from her pocket. It was a little piece of sunlight. Just as the Sun was rising, she'd made her move. She jumped up high and grabbed a bit. She thought of it as her **reward**.

Heads Up!

What do you think Sally Ann will do with the little piece of sunlight she grabs?

Now she threw the sunlight in the stove. She warmed her face and hands.

Then Sally Ann cooked up a batch of pancakes. She cooked two hundred for her. And she cooked two hundred and one for Death-Hug. It was the best breakfast they'd ever had.

Will the Real Sally Ann Please Stand Up?

Sally Ann lived in the 1800s. Back then, most Americans lived on the East Coast. Slowly, some **pioneers** moved west. They built homes where few people lived—on the wild frontier.

There are many tall tales about men who braved the wild frontier. And stories about Davy Crockett are some of the most famous. But there weren't too many about woman pioneers. That's another reason Sally Ann is so special.

Here's how the stories about Sally Ann got started. When Davy Crockett was away from home, Sally would write him letters. In her letters, she told great tales. She told him how she could jump over her own shadow. Or how she could scream louder than a mountain lion.

Of course, these stories weren't exactly true. They were **exaggerations**. Maybe she told these wild tales to herself to feel brave. Male or female, a person had to be mighty tough to survive life on the wild frontier.

Glossary

bolt *(verb)* to run quickly (p. 19)

brave *(adjective)* without fear in the face of danger (p. 9)

character *(noun)* having strong values and living by them (p. 17)

exaggeration *(noun)* a statement that goes beyond the truth (p. 37)

fierce *(adjective)* very strong (p. 23)

frontier *(noun)* recently settled land (p. 29)

holler *(verb)* to yell (p. 25)

pioneer *(noun)* a person who is one of the first to move to a new land and settle there (p. 37)

ragged *(adjective)* rough, uneven (p. 15)

reward *(noun)* a prize or gift (p. 35)

shriek *(verb)* to scream or make a loud, whining sound (p. 13)

shudder *(verb)* to shake (p. 15)

spirit *(noun)* a person's nature (p. 27)

streetcar *(noun)* a bus that runs on tracks (p. 19)